Comprehe

Book 2
John Davis

HOPSCOTCH
EDUCATIONAL PUBLISHING

Published by Hopscotch
A division of MA Education Ltd
St Jude's Church
Dulwich Road
Herne Hill
London SE24 0PB

Tel: 020 7738 5454

© 2007 MA Education Ltd

Written by John Davis
Series design by Blade Communications
Cover illustration by Susan Hutchison
Illustrated by David Burroughs
Printed by Colorman (Ireland) Ltd

ISBN 1-904307-21-3
ISBN13 978-1-904307-21-1

John Davis hereby asserts his moral right to be identified as the
author of this work in accordance with the Copyright, Designs
and Patents Act, 1988.

The National Literacy Strategy Framework – Text level links for Year 4

		T1	T2	T3	T4	T5	T6	T7	T8	T9	T10	T11	T12	T13	T14	T15	T16	T17	T18	T19	T20	T21	T22	T23	T24	T25	T26	T27
Term 1	Activity 1	•														•												
	Activity 2		•													•												
	Activity 3					•								•														
	Activity 4	•																										
	Activity 5	•																										
	Activity 6	•																										
	Activity 7	•											•															
	Activity 8	•																										
	Activity 9		•																									
	Activity 10								•																			
	Activity 11																					•						
	Activity 12																				•					•		
	Activity 13																						•				•	
	Activity 14																						•				•	
	Activity 15																	•										
	Activity 16																•											
	Activity 17																•											
	Activity 18																			•								
	Activity 19																•											
	Activity 20																•											
Term 2	Activity 21	•																										
	Activity 22	•																										
	Activity 23			•																								
	Activity 24					•																						
	Activity 25						•																					
	Activity 26				•																							
	Activity 27		•																									
	Activity 28																											
	Activity 29					•																						
	Activity 30				•																							
	Activity 31																									•		
	Activity 32																					•						
	Activity 33																•											
	Activity 34																•	•										
	Activity 35																•		•					•				
	Activity 36														•													
	Activity 37																						•					
	Activity 38																						•					
	Activity 39																				•							
	Activity 40																						•					
Term 3	Activity 41								•																			
	Activity 42			•																								
	Activity 43	•																										
	Activity 44	•																										
	Activity 45			•																								
	Activity 46		•						•																			
	Activity 47							•																				
	Activity 48			•																								
	Activity 49							•																				
	Activity 50			•																								
	Activity 51																				•							
	Activity 52																				•							
	Activity 53																		•									
	Activity 54																					•						
	Activity 55																		•									
	Activity 56																					•						
	Activity 57																		•									
	Activity 58																					•						
	Activity 59																									•		
	Activity 60																									•		

Today, more than ever, it is important that children can read and interpret text in many different forms. Traditional narrative is still important but, increasingly, vital information is now presented in a wide range of formats including graphs, flow charts, diagrams, timelines, pictures and illustrations. The overwhelming abundance of information available from internet sources places increasing demands on children to locate, sort, understand and interpret information more quickly than ever before. This series aims to help children develop strategies that will enable them to succeed in our information-overloaded world!

About this series

Comprehension is a series of books aimed at developing key comprehension skills across Key Stage 2 and the first years of Key Stage 3.

The series aims to set the children thinking. It requires them not only to interpret what they read but to use the information they have gathered in a constructive way, by applying it to, for example, graphs, maps, diagrams, pictures and tables. Alternatively, many of the activities require the children to explain in words information that is contained in different visual representations, such as graphs, diagrams and illustrations. The *Comprehension* series aims to stimulate children so that they see things from a different perspective and respond in a variety of ways.

There are four books in the series. Each book is matched to the National Literacy Strategy's *Framework for Teaching* as set out below, but we are confident that the books are flexible enough to be used across the age ranges from Year 3 to Year 8.

     Book 1 – Year 3
     Book 2 – Year 4
     Book 3 – Year 5
     Book 4 – Year 6

Each book aims to:
❑ develop children's inferential skills, encouraging them to 'read between the lines' where they have to search for hidden clues or make a link between cause and effect;
❑ develop children's deductive skills, enabling them to relate information in the text to their own experiences and background knowledge;
❑ develop children's evaluative skills to encourage critical evaluation and expression of opinion;
❑ support teachers by providing a programme that can be matched term by term to the NLS *Framework for Teaching* or can be 'dipped into' as and when required;
❑ encourage enjoyment and curiosity as well as develop skills of interpretation and response.

Each book is divided into ten fiction and ten non-fiction activities per term. These are listed on page 3, together with the *Framework's* Text level objective/s that each activity addresses.

Many of the activities are cross-curricular, taking in aspects of science, history and geography, for example. Other activities are centred around the interests of children, and topics such as magic, Martians, wizards and dragons are included. All the activities are intended to be fun as well as purposeful!

Using the activities

The activities are versatile enough to be used as part of whole-class lessons, group work or homework /reinforcement tasks. The teacher's role is to introduce the activity, carry out any revision of terms that may be necessary and put the task into a suitable context. Many of the activities would benefit from being discussed in pairs or small groups before commencing.

It is important to stress to the children that they read the complete text (including the required tasks) before they actually do anything. This helps to ensure they understand what they have to do before they begin. Their answers could be formulated in note form before reading through the activity again to make sure there has been no misunderstanding.

Name _____

The den

Every gang has to have a hideout or den for their meeting place. The three children decided to use the old, deserted garden shed among trees and dense undergrowth at the bottom of the garden.

The shed was square in shape and was made from wooden slats. The roof sloped slightly towards the back and had been covered in light green felt to make it waterproof.

The door, fastened with a metal latch and held on by three hinges, was at the front on the right-hand side. To the left of the door was a large rectangular window made up of twelve small panes of glass. Four of these were broken and the flower-patterned curtains inside could be seen flapping in the breeze.

An old rusty bicycle with one wheel missing and no saddle was propped up against the right-hand side of the shed near the door. On the other side a small oak tree had begun to sprout.

In an effort to brighten up its appearance the gang members had painted the shed. The door was bright red and the rest of the outside had been coloured light brown. Over the door hung a notice on which was written the words KEEP OUT MEMBERS ONLY in green capital letters on a white background but some of the paint had run and this gave the letters a rather streaky look.

❑ Read the description of the den. Draw an accurate picture of the den and its surroundings. Remember to use the correct colours where they are given.

Name _____

Thor's challenge

❑ This is a famous legend about the Viking god, Thor. The paragraphs are in the wrong order. Number them to show the correct order.

Thor chose a drinking contest. The servants of the giants brought in a large drinking horn apparently full of beer. It was not wide but it was long and narrow and the point at the end disappeared into the shadows at the side of the Great Hall. Thor raised the horn to his lips and began to drink.

When they saw the result of Thor's labours, the giants fell about laughing. One of them grabbed the horn and shouted, 'You may think you are a mighty god but you are obviously not much of a drinker. We have won the contest easily.'

Amid noisy gulps and swallows and with some coughing and spluttering, Thor drank down as much as he could. He was determined to finish off the liquid in the horn but when he eventually stopped to take breath he realised the level of the beer had hardly gone down at all.

Thor was in a good mood. There was nothing he liked better than a new challenge. He was fed up with fighting only dragons and serpents and now he was off to try his luck with the giants in the Great Hall.

Thor growled with anger and immediately snatched the horn back again to make another attempt. This time he swallowed longer and harder and held his breath for so long that he began to feel quite faint. When he set the horn down again the level had hardly changed, and to make matters worse there was a strong salty taste in his mouth like seawater.

As the door to the Great Hall was already open, Thor marched boldly in and announced his arrival. 'I am the famous Thor of Asgard,' he said, 'and I have come to challenge you to a trial of endurance and strength.' To Thor's anger the giants just laughed. 'What!' one of them shouted. 'A little squirt like you. This will be a poor contest but you choose first.'

It took over a month of hard travelling to find the place where the giants lived. The impressive walls of the Great Hall stood in front of Thor – as tall and as solid as a mountain range. For a moment he seemed nervous and apprehensive. But he composed himself, gripped his hammer tightly and said aloud, 'No more waiting about. It is time to get down to business.'

❑ Now draw a cartoon style storyboard to show the main events and the order in which they happened.

Name _____

Cry wolf

❏ This is the story of the boy who cried 'Wolf!' written as a play script.

1. The words inside the brackets are called stage directions. They tell the actors what they have to do on stage. Most of them are missing. Write in the other stage directions that are needed.

The boy is looking after sheep on a hillside outside the village but it is too quiet and too lonely and he gets bored. He decides to play a game, so he rushes back to the village.

Boy: Help! Help! Come quickly. I have seen a wolf and he is about to attack the sheep!

First villager: Hurry back to the sheep!

Second villager: We will come too and help you scare the wolf away.
(The villagers and some others follow the boy back up the hill to the sheep.)

First villager: I can't see any wolf.

Second villager: The sheep appear to be fine. Nothing has attacked them.
(The boy laughs loudly.)

Boy: I have played a trick on you. There was no wolf here at all.
(...)

Boy: What a good trick that was. Let's try it again. (...)

Boy: Help! Help! The wolf really was there. It was hiding behind a rock and you could not see it!

First villager: He could be right. We had better check to make certain.
(...)

Second villager: There is no wolf. He has played a trick on us again.
(...)

Boy: My trick seems to be working well. It is the best afternoon I have had for weeks.
(...)

Boy: Help! Help! The wolf has come this time, honestly. The sheep are in danger.

First villager: You have already made us look silly twice today.

Boy: I'm sorry. Please come. I am really telling the truth this time.

Second villager: No. We're staying here. We have had enough of your lies.
(...)

---

2. Write down how you think the story might have ended.

3. What do you think happened to the sheep? Did the boy learn his lesson?

Name _____

Bicycle parts

If you take a pair of wheels
and a saddle
and some tyres.
And you take some brakes
and spokes
and a lot of little wires.
And you take a set of bars
to help you steer with ease.
And you take a chain to drive it all
for power when you please.

If you take a set of pedals
and a bell
and some cogs.
Plus a set of valves
and gears
and some springs for when it jogs.
And you put them all together,
and you don't forget the oil
you can travel down the country lanes
for mile on happy mile.

1. Circle each word in the poem that names an important part of a bicycle.

2. On the bicycle frame below, draw and label all the missing parts named in the poem. Using a coloured pencil, add any other key parts that you think are missing from the poem.

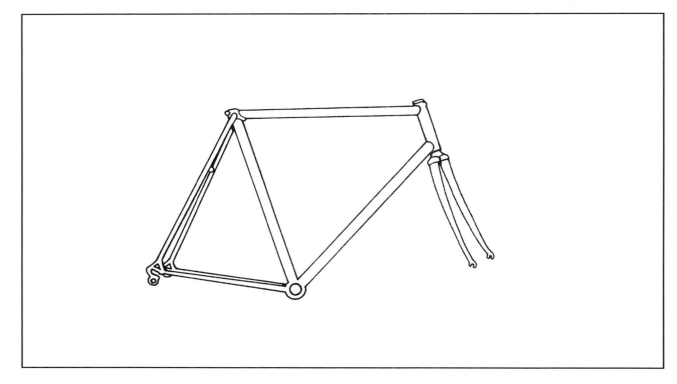

Name _____

Viking warrior

Thorkel stepped out of the longship and stood knee deep in the cold water of the English Channel. First his eyes scanned the empty sandy beach ahead of him and then he glanced back over his shoulder to watch the other longships in the fleet glide safely towards the shore.

The wind off the sea was chill, and he was glad of the warmth of the thick long-sleeved woollen tunic that came down almost to his knees. Tight woollen trousers covered his legs and on his feet he wore shoes made of goat skin.

As one of the leaders of the raiding party, Thorkel wore a chain mail suit over his woollen tunic. Thousands of hand-made iron rings had been linked together to make it but he was young and strong and used to its weight. His iron helmet had extra pieces to protect his eyes and nose and he would be grateful for this in the fighting that was to follow.

The weapons he carried would play their part too. In his left hand he gripped a battle-axe with its solid curved blade mounted on a wooden shaft just over a metre long. Tucked into his leather belt was his iron sword. It was a present from his father and its handle was decorated with silver and gold. In his right hand he held a round red shield that had been made of planks of wood joined together. The centre boss was of iron and a metal rim around its outer edge gave added strength.

❑ This extract is from a story about Thorkel, a member of a Viking raiding party that attacked England in about 800AD.

1. Underline in colour all the important words and phrases in the text that describe what Thorkel is wearing and the weapons he is carrying. Then use them to correctly label the picture of the Viking warrior that is shown.

2. Predict what you think might happen next to Thorkel and his fellow Vikings.

Name _____

Look for the clues

❑ Read each of the following short paragraphs. Then answer the questions after each one and give the reasons for your choice.

In the beautiful city of Venice, Paula and Adrian spent most of their holiday sightseeing. They especially enjoyed their trips in a gondola. Much of the city could be viewed as they made their way through the large network of canals.

*Is a **gondola** a bicycle, a taxi, a long narrow boat or a horse drawn carriage?*

As he trudged up the steep hill, the rucksack on Sanjay's back seemed to get heavier and heavier. He wished he had not packed so many clothes. Even the half-empty water bottle was proving to be too heavy.

*Does the word **trudged** mean 'walking wearily', 'running', 'walking quickly' or 'hopping'?*

After climbing the rocky peaks they were glad to descend into the glen where the land was flatter and easier on the feet. The stream was swollen from rain but they were able to cross, using large flat boulders as stepping stones.

*Is a **glen** the top of a mountain, a field for grazing cows, a wide footpath or a mountain valley?*

The two children collected their racquets and box of balls from the clubhouse, spent several minutes adjusting the net and then waited beside the court until their friends arrived.

Are the children going to play hockey, tennis, football or golf?

The police agreed that Mrs Jones was not a very reliable witness to the accident as she had been looking out of her lounge window that was over 20 metres above the level of the street.

Does Mrs Jones live in a bungalow, a detached house, a flat or a terraced house?

The best of the flowers were now just over in the garden and Leah and Nina spent most of the day helping their mother sweep up the leaves that had been blown on to the lawn by the chilly wind.

What time of year do you think it is. Springtime, the beginning of autumn, the middle of the summer or the winter?

Name _____

Treasure Island

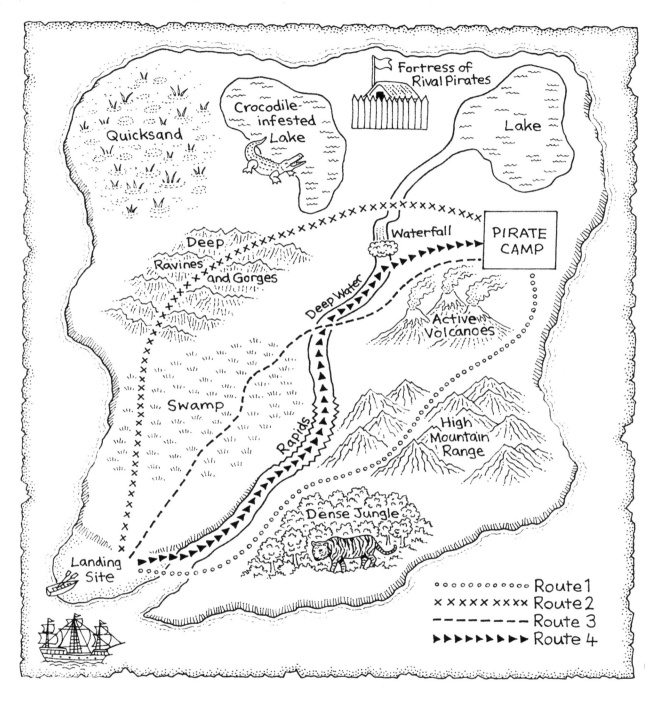

❑ Captain Patch and his band of pirates come ashore at the landing site and need to reach their camp on the other side of the island.

1. Look carefully at the map and describe what dangers they face if they follow each of the four routes shown.

2. What route would you follow if you were Captain Patch? Give your reasons.

Name _____

Police appeal

Westshire Constabulary Murder Squad

Preliminary murder report from SOCO (Scene of Crimes Officer)

Name: Detective Constable Bruce Wayne

Date: October 13th 1998

Location: Block of flats on Newtown Estate, Westshire. Third floor.
Flat Number 19. Name on door – Mr A Mann.

Scene of crime details: Body found in the living room. Face down on the mat
by the television. Gas fire blazing. Room very messy. Two chairs turned over,
table lamp lying smashed on the floor, windows wide open and curtains
flapping in the wind. Drawers and cupboards open with contents lying all over
the floor. Blood stains close to the body. No sign of murder weapon. CD player
on with volume up high.

Description of body: Young Caucasian woman. Slim build. Short dark hair.
Lying face down with right arm under the body and left arm outstretched.
Wearing white T-shirt and blue jeans. Butterfly tattoo visible on left
forearm. No shoes. Small shoulder bag open on nearby table near the
television. Purse, mobile phone, notebook, credit cards, brush and piece of
tissue lying on the table and surrounding floor.

❏ Detective Constable Wayne will
soon have to appear on local
television and radio stations to ask
people in the town for their help in
catching the murderer. Write a script
for him to use. Decide what he
needs to tell people about the
identity of the murder victim, what
clues he might need help with and
other ways in which members of the
public might be able to help.

Name _____

Wanted: Dead or Alive!

$2,000 REWARD! DEAD OR ALIVE!

The sheriff and his deputies in the town of Dry Gulch, and the Board of Directors of the First Central Bank are offering a reward of $2,000 for the capture, dead or alive, of **JOHN WESLEY BOSTON** also known as **BLACK JACK BOSTON**. In the company of others – still to be identified - Boston held up the First Central Bank in Dry Gulch at around noon on February 17th 1886 and stole a total of $14,700 in assorted notes and coins. During the raid and in order to make good his escape, Boston shot and killed Mr Jed Foster, a guard at the bank, who attempted to arrest him.

DESCRIPTION

JOHN WESLEY BOSTON is six foot three inches tall and weighs in the region of 224 pounds. He is 25 years old with a light complexion, although he often goes for days without shaving. He has blue eyes and light brown hair that tends to look darker because he uses a lot of hair oil. Boston has a habit of blinking frequently when talking to someone. He usually wears a black hat with dark woollen clothes including a checked shirt and leather waistcoat. There is a narrow gold ring on the middle finger of his right hand. He wears a size 9 cowboy boot with a pair of fancy silver spurs that jangle when he walks. He moves around with a slight limp in his left leg caused by a fall from a horse when he was a child. He has a long thin face but a rather short thick nose. His top lip tends to curl up and his ears stick out prominently. Boston often walks in a casual way with both hands stuck deep into his pockets. He is known as a good horseman and has a particular fondness for white horses. He always carries two matching silver .55 calibre pistols and is regarded as one of the best shots in the territory.

1. In your own words say who the wanted poster is for and what crime he has committed.
2. Why do you think the reward money is so high and why do you think John Wesley Boston is wanted dead or alive?
3. What items of his clothing or equipment might particularly help people to recognise him? Describe them.
4. If he wore other clothes or put on a disguise in what other ways might he still be recognised?

Name _____

What the Dickens?

Charles John Huffam Dickens, often described as one of Britain's greatest story-writers, was born in Portsmouth in 1812.

Five years later the family moved to Chatham in Kent and in 1824 Dickens was sent to work in a blacking factory when his father was arrested for getting into debt. Later, Dickens became a clerk in a solicitor's office and a reporter on several newspapers.

In the same year that he married his wife, Catherine – 1836 – Dickens published his first book called *The Sketches of Boz* describing life in London at that time. The following year the book that established his reputation, *The Pickwick Papers*, came out and after that followed *Oliver Twist* (1838) and *Nicholas Nickleby* (1839).

The well-known story about the miser Scrooge and the visit of the three spirits, *A Christmas Carol*, came out in 1843, the year after Dickens and his wife, Catherine, went on a tour of North America.

For three years from 1844 the Dickens family lived in Italy and then Switzerland and France, but they moved back to England and in 1856 Dickens bought a house at Gad's Hill near Chatham where he was to spend most of the rest of his life.

Other books written at this time include *David Copperfield* (1850) *Bleak House* (1852) and *Hard Times* (1854). From 1853 onwards Dickens toured theatres in many parts of the country giving public readings of his stories.

In the last ten years of his life, Dickens wrote other famous novels like *A Tale of Two Cities* (1859) and *Great Expectations* (1861). In 1869 he started work on *The Mystery of Edwin Drood* but he died the year after and the book was never finished. Dickens had asked to be buried in Rochester but it was felt more appropriate that he should be buried with other famous writers in Westminster Abbey.

❑ Make a timeline model to show what you think are the most important events in the life of the writer Charles Dickens.

Name _____

What a story!

HOW MANY MORE?   *CLIPPER HOLDS*   ***KIDS LEARN***
                            LEAD   ***DIY LESSON***

STAR GUEST   MARKET EVENT
CUTS THE RIBBON   **FIRE DAMAGES**   TAKES THE BISCUIT
                        HEALTH UNIT

CLEAR   SUCCESS STORY
IMPROVEMENT   COMES TO TOWN
                        HOLIDAY HITCH

WRITE ON!   **MILLION POUND**
                        JOINING FORCES   **WINNERS**

HAIR RAISING   **RIGHT UP MY STREET**
MOMENT   CHECK THE GAS

❏ Look carefully at the newspaper headlines above and then match them to
  the correct story in the list below.

1. An author publishes a new book on their local town.
2. Accidents keep happening at the same road junction.
3. Two clothing firms are to merge into one company.
4. A family was held up by a plane delay in Spain.
5. A blaze wrecks the equipment in a local hospital.
6. A large sailing ship takes the lead in a long distance race at sea.
7. Office workers shave off their hair to raise money for charity.
8. A television personality opens a new supermarket.
9. A neighbourhood watch organiser talks to local homeowners.
10. A local couple win a large prize on the lottery.
11. Workmen are shown how to double glaze windows.
12. Faulty cookers and fires may be very dangerous.
13. Children are taught how to make useful things at a superstore.
14. A highly successful new musical is to visit a local theatre.
15. Housewives sell off their tasty home-made food.

Name _____

Headline writer

❑ Here are the first sentences of twelve stories that are to appear in a newspaper. Make up your own headlines to go with them. Decide on the size and style of lettering and make them short and snappy. Remember the purpose of headlines is to encourage people to read the story.

1. A thief got into the changing rooms during Edwell Town's football match on Saturday and went through the players' belongings.

2. A long-awaited new car park was due to open in Ashton Street today.

3. Plans went on show this week for one of the biggest housing schemes in the Downton area for years.

4. Businesses are being recruited for a new project to help pupils at local schools with maths lessons.

5. A driver was injured when his car collided with a fire engine yesterday.

6. Hundreds of cyclists took to their bikes to celebrate European Car Free Day.

7. Langdon Cathedral Girls' Choir held a special service on Sunday to celebrate its tenth anniversary.

8. Train services in the Rownhill area have slightly improved, according to the latest figures.

9. Southwold Primary School has appointed a new headteacher.

10. A Jack Russell terrier was recovering today after spending five days trapped underground.

11. A lorry full of potatoes crashed into an ambulance before skidding into the side of a house.

12. Fish have returned to a lake in Westville Park after a major clean up of the water.

Name _____

Tasty snack

Cheese on toast is a quick and tasty snack that can be eaten at any time of the day.

The things you need to make it, called the ingredients, are bread, butter, cheese and some sauce or pickle. You will also need some items of kitchen equipment. These are a cheese grater and a knife and of course you will need to use the grill section of an oven.

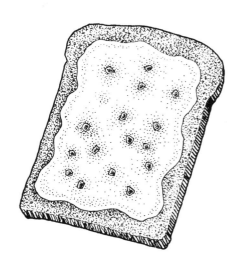

To start with, find some slices of bread, put them under a hot grill and toast them on both sides. When this is complete, butter should be spread on one side of the bread only.

Cut a piece of cheese and use the grater to break it up into fine pieces. When this is complete, sprinkle the cheese on top of the side of the toast that has already been buttered.

The slices of toast should then be placed back under the grill and should remain there until the cheese has started to melt. When they are ready, remove the items from under the grill and add either sauce or pickle to complete the dish. Place on a plate and eat with a knife and fork.

❑ Using bullet points for each item, make three different lists to help people who want to make cheese on toast.

Ingredients	**Equipment**	**Instructions**
•	•	•
•	•	•
•	•	•
•	•	•
•	•	•
•	•	•
•	•	•

Name _____

A watery home

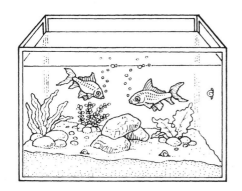

Fish such as goldfish should not be kept in small bowls. They should live in a wide tank where the large surface area of water will ensure they get a good supply of oxygen. Buy a good-sized tank and spend several days preparing it carefully.

First, when you have made sure it is perfectly clean, place a layer of gravel or coarse sand over the bottom. It is recommended that the gravel or sand is sloped slightly from one side to the other. This means scraps of uneaten food will fall down to one side and can be taken out easily.

The next step is to fill the tank with water – rainwater or pond water is best. Then fix a few water plants in the sand. These not only make the fish feel at home but will also give out oxygen and help to keep the water clean. Small pebbles and interesting shaped rocks can also be put onto the bottom of the tank. This will make a more natural looking habitat for the fish. It is important that these are scrubbed clean first in case they have materials on them that could be harmful to your goldfish.

At this stage you could add some water snails. You can buy them from your garden centre. They will also help to create a natural and clean environment for your fish.

Now your goldfish home is almost ready. Position it somewhere in the room where it will get plenty of light, but not direct sunlight. Close to, but not beside, a window will probably be best.

Finally, comes the exciting part. Several days later, visit the pet centre and buy your goldfish. Check with an expert there to see how many fish can live comfortably in the size of tank you have. Carry the fish home carefully and introduce them gently to the tank. If you have made their home properly they will be happy and healthy and should live for many years.

❏ Read the information carefully. Draw a series of pictures in the correct order to show the instructions. You should choose the number of pictures to use – it could be six, eight, ten or even more.

Name _____

Accident report

❏ This chart gives the number of children injured in road accidents in one year.

Pedestrians:

Age group	0-4 years	5-9 years	10-14 years
killed	98	254	127
serious injuries	965	3,674	2,729
slight injuries	2,780	9,864	7,953

Cyclists:

Age group	0-4 years	5-9 years	10-14 years
killed	4	32	84
serious injuries	19	492	1,364
slight injuries	56	1,298	6,003

1. Which age group had the highest number of fatal accidents?

2. Which age group among the pedestrians had the most accidents overall?

3. Which age group among the cyclists had the most accidents overall?

4. Why do you think the age group 5–9 had the most accidents in the pedestrian section?

5. Why do you think the age group 10–14 had the most accidents in the cyclist section?

6. Why do you think the fewest accidents came in the 0–4 age range?

7. Suggest ways in which the accident numbers in the 5–9 age range might be improved.

8. Suggest ways in which the accident numbers in the 10–14 age range might be improved.

Name _____

Egyptian army

❑ Information can sometimes be organised in the form of a hierarchy. A hierarchy is a pyramid of power in which people are sorted in order of importance. Usually there is one leader at the top, several leading people below them, greater numbers in the next rank, more below that and so on.

❑ Here is some information about the set up of power in the army in Ancient Egypt. Convert this information into a hierarchy pyramid with each level getting wider as it moves towards the base of the shape. Decide how many levels are needed and label each one carefully. You could draw a suitable picture to illustrate each of the levels.

Society in Ancient Egypt was organised along the lines of social class. Once you were born into a certain class, you remained there for the rest of your life and it was very difficult to move from one class to another.

The Egyptians were united into one nation around 3100BC and they then fought and conquered peoples in what is now Libya, Syria and Iraq. At the top of the army hierarchy was the Pharaoh or god-king. He was the wealthiest person, owned all the large palaces and much of the best land. He told everyone what to do and had the power of life and death over all his subjects.

Below him came the generals. There were only a few of these and they were usually related to the Pharaoh, being either his sons or his brothers. They made all the important decisions on the battlefield, especially if the Pharaoh was not taking part in the battle himself.

Taking orders from the generals were the lower ranking military officers. They were also important people like noblemen. They were in charge of a squad of soldiers, were closely involved in the hand-to-hand fighting and were responsible for leading their men into action. Also included in this section would be the scribes who wrote dispatches and records of the different campaigns. The next group was the charioteers who worked in pairs and were often a father and son combination. They rode on two-wheeled wooden chariots usually pulled by a pair of horses.

Under these came the archers who fired on the enemy and tried to kill as many as possible. The bow and arrow was just about the only method in those days of killing or wounding an enemy at long range. The archers did their work before the final group and the lowest order, the foot soldiers, went into action. They wore no armour and had to defend themselves with large wooden shields. These soldiers were tough, well fed and fit and fought with axes, swords and spears.

Name _____

The Beaufort scale

Wind speed is measured on the Beaufort scale. It was invented in 1806 by an English admiral, Sir Francis Beaufort, who realised that a simple way to judge wind speed was to compare the way sailing ships must be rigged in different winds.

His scale had 13 wind strengths, with calm at Force 0 and hurricane at Force 12. The scale has been adapted for use on land, using indicators like rising smoke, breaking trees and falling chimneys.

When the air is calm, smoke will rise vertically from a chimney. Light air or Force 1 will move smoke gently away from the direction the wind is coming from and a light breeze, Force 2, can be felt on the face.

Leaves and small twigs on trees will be in constant motion and light flags will flap when Force 3 or a gentle breeze is blowing. When the breeze becomes moderate, Force 4, dust and light paper will get blown about and small branches on trees will move. At Force 5, a fresh breeze, small trees in leaf will begin to sway and inland stretches of water like lakes will begin to have crested waves.

People will have trouble using umbrellas if a strong breeze, also known as Force 6, develops and a moderate gale, Force 7, means that pedestrians have to bend forward to walk in the wind. Force 8, described as a fresh gale, causes twigs to break off trees and a strong gale, Force 9, results in damage to chimney pots and roof tiles on properties.

Conditions become even more serious during a whole gale, Force 10, with trees uprooted and buildings damaged. There is widespread damage and destruction when a storm, Force 11, rages and large scale havoc and disaster can be expected when a Force 12 hurricane comes hurtling in.

❏ Use the information to draw a three-column grid to show the Beaufort Scale.

Force	Name	Description
0	calm	

Name _____

Fact or opinion

❑ Read through this version of the story of The Gunpowder Plot. Draw a line down the middle of a piece of paper. Write the headings FACTS on one side and OPINIONS on the other. As you read, pick out what you feel are the main points of the story and sort them into the two groups.

The Gunpowder Plot happened about 400 years ago in November 1605. The king at that time was James 1 who was to rule for a total of 22 years. England in 1605 was a dangerous place to live. James 1 was a good king but all the followers of a religion, who were called Roman Catholics, wanted to have him killed because he was treating them badly.

The Catholics, led by a cowardly man called Robert Catesby, decided to blow up the king and all of his friends when they went to the Houses of Parliament, which are in London. With the king dead they hoped to have a new monarch who would be kinder to the Catholics.

The plotters met in secret places to work on their plan. They contacted a man called Guy Fawkes who was a brave soldier and an expert at using gunpowder. They asked him to organise the explosion. He had to put barrels of gunpowder under the Houses of Parliament and to make sure there was enough gunpowder to kill everyone in the building.

For months everything went well. The barrels of gunpowder were taken into the cellars under the building and Guy Fawkes was ready to light them with a candle when the time came. Then one of the plotters got frightened. He wrote a letter to one of his relations warning him not to go to the Houses of Parliament with the others. The letter did not spell out the plot in detail but, reading between the lines, it was not difficult to realise what it meant.

The letter was shown to King James, the cellars were then searched and Guy Fawkes was arrested as he was checking the barrels of gunpowder. Later when he was tortured he told the king's soldiers the names of the other plotters and many of them were captured or killed.

Guy Fawkes and some of his friends were put on trial in January 1606 for plotting to kill the king. The case against them was very strong. They were found guilty and later executed as an example to show everyone what would happen to people who tried to get rid of the king. Rather than improving the situation, things got worse for Catholics following the plot and harsh laws were passed that made them suffer even more.

Name _____

Choosing a home

Five villages cluster round the market town of Deepdale. Four of them, Denhill, Alnthorp, Rigsby and Chestham are built among the hills while Moorcroft is built on flat land. Rigsby and Denhill both have primary schools and Alnthorp is the only village with a shop. The area's only post office is at Moorcroft and the railway station is at Rigsby which is also situated close to Tarnside Lake. All the villages are on bus routes to Deepdale and there are football and cricket playing facilities in Denhill, Alnthorp and Moorcroft. A golf course is being developed at Denhill and is due to open soon.

❏ Use ticks and crosses to complete the checklist given in the grid below.

	Denhill	Alnthorp	Rigsby	Chestham	Moorcroft
hills					
flat land					
schools					
shop					
post office					
station					
lake					
bus route					
football/cricket					
golf course					

❏ The people listed below are looking for new homes in one of the five villages. Which village would be the most suitable for them? Give your reasons.

Mr Patel: He is over 70 years of age and finds it difficult to walk very far these days. He needs to be near a post office so he can collect his weekly pension easily. Mr Patel likes to visit friends and relations by bus.

Mr and Mrs Carter: They have three young children. The family likes to walk in the countryside at weekends. Mr Carter likes to watch live sport when he can and Mrs Carter hopes to take up a new outdoor sporting hobby as soon as possible.

Sally Jones: She is hoping to buy her first home. She has no car but needs to make regular business trips to London and Birmingham. Sally is particularly interested in wildlife and spends her spare time photographing and drawing water birds and plants.

Name _____

Roman roads

❑ The Romans were superb engineers and built excellent roads. Roads were essential to them for moving the army around the Empire. They also became important trading routes. The Romans tried to make their roads take the shortest, straightest route between two places. Our word 'mile' comes from the Latin word 'mille' which means a thousand. A Roman mile was 1,000 paces (about 1,500 metres).

❑ The labelled diagram below shows a cross-section of how the Romans constructed their roads. In your own words, explain in detail how they were built including all the important features.

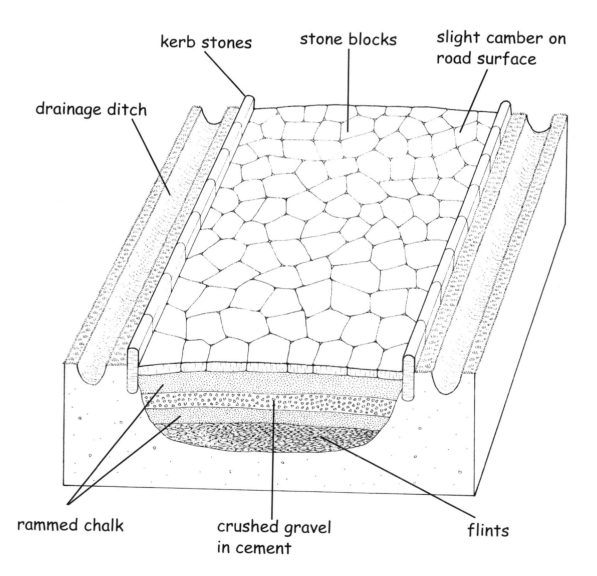

kerb stones   stone blocks   slight camber on road surface

drainage ditch

rammed chalk   crushed gravel in cement   flints

Name _____

Strange planet

A spacecraft from Earth approaches an unknown planet in the far reaches of the galaxy and prepares to land.

The sky all around was clear and shone with a brilliant white light. The surface of the planet looked barren, deserted and sandy. There was no evidence of any urgently needed supplies of water. Nothing moved and no life seemed apparent. A strong wind picked up every so often and carried with it dusty clouds of the arid yellow sand.

High above the planet in the spacecraft, the crew peered out of portholes anxious to see what awaited them at the end of their 375,000,000 kilometre journey. They had circled the planet several times before coming in to land and with no life forms visible they had decided to take the chance.

The pilot scanned the planet's surface for the most suitable landing site, hoping the sand would not prove to be too soft when the final impact occurred. The bank of small rockets under the spacecraft fired to slow down its descent and a parachute burst open above to help ease it gently down.

This routine had been practised so many times in training that it went without a hitch. Slowly the craft descended. It hovered just above the surface, its rockets turning the dusty sand into a swirling whirlwind. Finally, its four legs touched down almost simultaneously and, apart from a slight metallic groan, all was silent.

While most of the crew busied themselves completing a range of technical tasks, two of them could not resist looking through a porthole to see if their arrival had caused any reaction. To their amazement two creatures suddenly appeared in front of them pressing their faces against the opening and staring directly into the craft with blank, expressionless faces.

❑ Which of the events below do you think might have happened when the spacecraft's door was opened? Explain your reasons for choosing it. Also give reasons why you think the others are unlikely to have happened.

1. The two aliens started to talk to the astronauts.
2. The two aliens offered the astronauts fresh supplies of water to drink.
3. The two aliens rushed forward waving guns and other kinds of dangerous weapons.
4. The two aliens approached slowly and carefully and began to talk to themselves in quiet voices.
5. The two aliens seemed to disappear as they were lost in the pitch blackness.

Name _____

Alien creature

Blapwits live on the planet Repsol. They are very large, powerful creatures that can grow up to six metres long and stand one metre off the ground at the shoulder.

The blapwit has the body of a crocodile complete with lashing tail. The head is small and round and it has a long neck rather like an elephant's trunk. Its four short legs are solid like tree trunks but it can move around quickly. The feet, which have five toes, are broad and webbed like a duck to help with swimming.

The whole of this alien creature's body is covered with purple scales that are triangular in shape and overlap for protection rather like the tiles on the roof of a house.

On the top of the head are three pointed ears that can swivel to pick up even the slightest sound. The eyes are small and dark and are at the front of the head. When the large jaws are opened, the creature displays two rows of sharp pointed teeth.

Blapwits live in the lakes and rivers of the dense jungle areas of Repsol. They are meat eaters but after a large meal can go for several weeks without food.

❑ Read through the description of the blapwit carefully. Draw a picture of it and label the drawing. Try to use a scale to give some idea of the creature's size.

Name _____

On location

❑ Here are the descriptions of places or settings
that come near the beginning of two
different stories. Read them through carefully
and then carry out the instructions given at
the bottom of the page.

The blue caravan was made entirely from wood. It stood in the corner of the
large field close to the hedge and nestled in the shelter of a large oak tree.
It was small, no bigger than the size of a large van, except it was rounded like
a barrel. Its two large wheels lifted it off the ground and the recently
painted entrance door at the front could only be reached by climbing a small
flight of stairs. There were small windows on both sides of the caravan and a
larger one at the back. All were open, and brightly coloured curtains could be
seen flapping in the breeze. In the middle of the caravan's roof there was a
short metal chimney pipe that puffed out a continual stream of white smoke.

The derelict old house was next to the graveyard and looked as if it had been
deserted for many years. Several tiles were missing from the tall pointed
roof, some of the grey stonework was loose and the gate at the entrance to
the path swung limply from its hinges. There were six stone steps leading up
to the front door which was covered with flaking paint. The building was
rectangular in shape with a curious mixture of square, arched and circular
windows. They were all tightly fastened and were so grimy that it was
impossible to see inside. Four large double chimney pots were fixed in
different places on the roof. They stood on the top of brick pillars and their
twisted shape made them one of the most attractive features of the house.

1. From the information given above draw accurate pictures of the two locations
   used in the stories.

2. List the main differences between the two places described. Are there any
   similarities between them at all?

3. In what type of stories do you think these two settings feature? What titles
   could they have? What characters might they include? Give reasons for your
   answers.

Name _____

A knight's tale

❑ Here is part of a narrative poem about the knights who lived in Britain many
centuries ago. Find the list of 'historical' and 'special' words that are given at
the bottom of the sheet and circle them in the text with a coloured pencil.
Then use the clues given in the rest of the poem to explain what you think
each of these words mean.

The knight spurred on his charger
He reached the castle gate
He lifted up his visor
And bid them set the date

When he returned days later
In the tournament to fight
He swore he would seek vengeance
Against the evil knight

The two men faced each other
As the jousting bout began
Weighed down with mace and lance and shield
The chargers gamely ran

They met with thundering clash of steel
And both knights fell to ground
They struggled up to fight by hand
As spectators crowded round

The blows came thick, the blows came fast
It was a close run thing
The weapons clashed, the armour groaned
With each metallic ring

The stranger struck the final blow
Bravery had banished fear
The evil knight was overthrown
All freemen raised a cheer.

knight   spurred   charger   visor   bid   tournament   vengeance

jousting   bout   mace   lance   armour   metallic   banished

overthrown   freemen

Name _____

Match winner

❏ This is a rhyming poem but some of the words have been left out. Read through the poem carefully and add suitable words in the spaces. They must fit the story and rhyme with the word at the end of the line above.

Listen now, I'll tell you true
About a girl whose name was _____
She was the fit and healthy kind
As active a youngster as you would _____
One day while partly in a dream
She joined the local football _____
The ball was hard, the pitch was bumpy
The manager was always _____
He told her where she had to play
But added, 'Keep right out of the _____
She tried defence, she tried attack
She played up front and at the _____
When someone else gave up the role
She even tried her luck in _____
She leapt and dived and sprang each time
But only gathered mud and _____

Then one sunny April day
When others said they could not _____
Our heroine, now known by name
Was picked for an important _____
The manager said, 'Play until you drop.
A win will take us to the _____
The game was close, the game was tough
The other side was very _____
They kicked at every chance they could
Knocking into players where they _____
A minute left and still no score
The crowd silent but ready to _____
A pass went to Sue, two metres out
She gave the leather a hefty _____
A better shot you could not get
As the ball flew into the empty _____

Name _____

In the mood

❑ Read these short descriptions. Decide what sort of mood the characters are in and why you think they are feeling like this. How would you feel in such circumstances? Suggest what you think they might do next.

Beth looked longingly at the leather collar and lead that still hung on its peg by the door. She remembered all those times when they had played together in the garden and in the local playing field, not to mention those long walks along the riverbank in the summertime. 'I miss him so much,' she said to Mum when caught during one of her quiet spells. 'I know, love,' was the reply, 'but he was nearly 15 years old and he had enjoyed a very happy life.'

Brothers! They were always taking things that did not belong to them and it always led to trouble. It had taken David a good six months to save up for the new game. All his friends at school had them a long time before he did and he had felt really left out. Then, only a few weeks after he had picked it up from the shop, it lay in several pieces on his bedroom carpet. 'Daniel!' David had shouted when he came home from school and discovered the mess. 'Get up here now.'

Claire had never been keen on the move. Well, who wanted to travel 200 kilometres to a new home, not know anyone when you got there and leave all your friends behind. Reluctantly she got ready on that first morning and forced down a little breakfast even though she was not feeling hungry. The journey to the new school was quiet. Dropped at the gate, she walked through the playground only too well aware of the halting conversations and the turning heads. She followed the signs to the headteacher's office and knocked on the door. 'I'm Claire Hopkins,' she announced when it was opened. 'I'm starting in Year Four today.'

Simon pulled back the piece of rusty corrugated iron that blocked the narrow doorway and peered inside. 'Aaron, Oliver, are you in there?' he shouted. 'You know we are not supposed to play around here.' He regretted not having reminded them before they ran off to hide. His parents were always telling him to keep away from the derelict factory. 'Come on, show yourselves,' he barked. Suddenly, away to his left, he heard the clink of loose stones being trodden on and in the half-light he could just make out the shadowy form of a figure.

Name _____

Rising tide

The hunt for fossils on the long pebbly shore had gone well, but now as the sun began to dip behind the cliff, Peter felt cold and a long way from home. Even though the rock samples they carried in their bags were small the total weight made them heavy and this had slowed them down in the last hour.

Peter stopped, pulled his coat tightly around him and gazed out to sea. The wind was beginning to whip up the waves and they crashed even louder onto the rocks in front of him. Spray flew into the air and foamy water washed around the large grey boulders. His sister Bethany had wandered a little way ahead of him. He called the little girl back, encouraged her to button up her raincoat and reminded her to stay close to him all the time.

Away to his right he watched for several moments as the sea rushed in towards the base of the cliff. Each wave seemed to move closer to the rocks and soon, if the tide continued to come in with such speed, they would become cut off from the safety of the sandy beach beyond. Taking his sister by the hand Peter began to quicken the pace but the rocks and pebbles were slippery with damp seaweed and on several occasions they stumbled and almost fell in their haste.

❏ Read the opening paragraphs of this story and answer the questions below.

1. Where do you think the story is set? What clues in the text give away the location? Do you think this is a good setting for a story? Explain your reasons.

2. Make a list of the main dangers that are facing the two children as the story opens.

3. What evidence is there that Peter is becoming concerned about the safety of his sister?

4. How do you think the children would be feeling in a situation like this? How would you feel personally?

5. Look at the words listed below that appear in the story. What other words might be used to replace them?

   dip   gazed   flew   base   boulders   stumbled

6. How do you think the story might develop after this opening scene? List six possible events that might happen if you had to continue the story through to the end.

Name _____

In a word

Lost parcel

It was a fine day so he decided to walk. At the gateway, David turned left and went to the corner before he decided to cross the road. He had felt unwell the day before but the rash on his chest had gone and now he was better. Going back to work would be the right thing to do. He saw no-one he knew on his way into town but he preferred to travel on his own. At the post office, the book he had wrapped to send to his son was weighed on the scales. He finally secured the parcel with a large elastic band and fixed on the stamps. The job seemed to be complete but when he got outside he remembered he had forgotten to hand it over the counter and had left it resting on the table.

Exotic pet

The most noticeable thing about Karen's new pet snake was its band of fine brightly coloured scales. It spent most of its time in an old wooden chest resting on the table to the right of the large window. It lay on a bed of soft felt. Karen first saw a picture of the snake in a book and from then on had always wanted one of her own. It was better than any others she had seen before. Karen sent for details through the post and after reading all the necessary information had bought one from the pet shop. It was the last one they had left. It made her cross when people said snakes were nasty and slimy. It had bitten her once on the back of the hand but generally it was harmless and did not mind being handled.

❑ These 15 words are found in both the short stories.

scales, left, right, band, post, felt, cross, fine, back, table, book, chest, saw, own, better

1. Underline them with a coloured pencil.

2. Then, when you have read the stories through, decide if the words mean the same or different things in each of them.

Name _____

Desert trek

❑ This extract of descriptive writing has been taken from a story about explorers in the desert. It is full of adjectives and adverbs (describing words) and similes (phrases that use 'like' or 'as' to describe something).

1. Underline the adjectives in red, the adverbs in blue and the similes in green. Then replace each one with suitable descriptive words and phrases of your own.

The golden sun shone brightly down as hot as fire as the two weary travellers plodded slowly through the fine sand. At this stage of the long day their rucksacks felt as heavy as lead and they looked forward anxiously to reaching the cool shade of the oasis.

As they looked ahead, shading their tired eyes carefully with their sunburnt hands, they could see the waterhole in the distance, its tall trees stretching up as green as grass.

'The refreshing water will be as clear as crystal,' said Ruth loudly. 'Luckily we do not have far to go.'

The remaining stretch of sand was as flat as a pancake so the brave explorers knew they should be able to make it easily. A good, sound sleep during the dark, cold night would leave them as fresh as a daisy and eagerly waiting for the next hard day.

But the more they increased the pace in order to reach the oasis quickly the further it seemed to move away. Was the oasis real or was it a mirage? Was the shimmering heat of the desert and their aching eyes playing strange tricks on them and were they further from safety than they realised?

Now it was Alison's turn to be as steady as a rock. 'Come on,' she urged Ruth confidently, 'we must keep going.'

2. Discuss what you think are the meaning of the words 'oasis' and 'mirage'.

Name _____

Canal rescue

❏ Read this opening section from a story involving a dramatic rescue and then answer the questions that are given at the bottom of the sheet.

Fifteen-year-old Sanjay Patel had been late leaving the music club at school and already it was quite dark. His parents had often reminded him not to use the path alongside the canal at night but he was cold, hungry and anxious to get home as soon as possible. If he took the short cut on this occasion who would know?

Although the canal area was dotted with streetlights, they were not bright and most of the path was covered with shadows from the overhanging trees. The wind whistled through their bare branches and stirred up the water on the surface of the canal.

Suddenly Sanjay thought he heard a low moaning sound. It seemed to come from the edge of the canal. At first he thought his imagination was playing tricks on him and he walked quickly on. But then he heard the same noise again and this time it stopped him in his tracks. He looked around him as his mouth grew dry and his heart started to beat faster.

The moan sounded a third time. Sanjay walked gingerly over to the water's edge, being careful not to slip on the mossy stones. He peered over the side and, as his eyes became more accustomed to the blackness around the water he could just make out the shape of a man clinging desperately to the slender branch of a bush that grew out from the canal wall.

1. Why do you think Sanjay's parents told him not to use the canal path?

2. How does the writer of the story gradually build up the tension?

3. What phrases help explain how Sanjay was feeling when he heard the sounds?

4. How do you think the man might have got into the canal?

5. Describe how you think the man might be feeling now.

6. Explain the meaning of the phrases 'his imagination was playing tricks on him' and 'stopped him in his tracks'.

7. List the main similarities and differences between a canal and a river.

8. Predict what action you think Sanjay might take next. What do you think he can do to help the man in this situation?

Name _____

League table

❏ This is the top of the County League. Teams are given three points for a win and one point for a draw.

	P	W	D	L	F	A	Pts	GD
Rushall	8	6	1	1	37	12	19	25
Christchurch	7	5	2	0	29	16	17	13
Hamworthy	8	4	4	0	30	17	16	13
Burnham	8	4	4	0	25	19	16	6
Bloomfield	6	4	0	2	28	24	12	4
Cleeve	8	3	3	2	19	21	12	-2
Blanford	8	2	3	3	15	26	9	-11
Maldon	8	1	5	2	12	30	8	-18

❏ Update the figures above to show the results of the matches below. Then re-order the teams to show their new positions.

Results

Christchurch	4	Selby	2
Cleeve	2	Bloomfield	2
Hamworthy	5	Boston	1
Burnham	0	Shildon	2
Hamble	3	Blanford	3
Rushall	1	Maldon	2

❏ Now answer the following questions.

1. Who leads the league now?

2. Who has scored most goals?

3. Who has let in most goals?

4. Who has the best goal difference?

5. Who has the worst goal difference?

6. Which teams are still unbeaten?

Name _____

The Green family

❏ Study this family tree of the Green family and then answer the questions below.

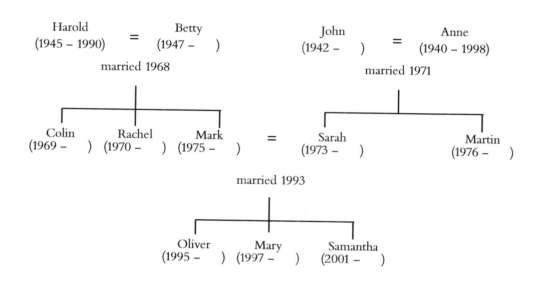

| Harold (1945 – 1990) | = | Betty (1947 –) | | John (1942 –) | = | Anne (1940 – 1998) |

married 1968   married 1971

Colin (1969 –)   Rachel (1970 –)   Mark (1975 –)   =   Sarah (1973 –)   Martin (1976 –)

married 1993

Oliver (1995 –)   Mary (1997 –)   Samantha (2001 –)

1. Which of the grandparents are still alive?

2. Who are the eldest and the youngest persons in the three generations?

3. How many children did Harold and Betty have?

4. How old was Sarah when she got married?

5. What are Mark's children's uncles called?

6. How old was Anne when she died?

7. How many years older than Samantha is Oliver?

8. What relation to each other are Rachel and Sarah?

Name _____

Daylight hours

❑ This timetable shows information for one day only in four cities in the British Isles.

The following symbols are used.

Sun   Lights

Place	rises sets		on off	
Belfast	7.48 am	6.15 pm	6.35 pm	7.39 am
Edinburgh	7.40 am	5.55 pm	6.27 pm	7.30 am
London	7.30 am	5.36 pm	6.16 pm	7.24 am
Cardiff	7.28 am	5.30 pm	5.55 pm	7.15 am

❑ Now answer the following questions.

1. Name the place where the Sun rises at a) half past seven b) almost ten minutes to eight.

2. Name the place where the Sun sets at a) quarter past six b) half past five.

3. Where does the Sun rise earliest?

4. Where does the Sun set latest?

5. In London, Belfast and Cardiff how soon after sunset should lights go on?

6. How many hours is the Sun in the sky over a) Edinburgh b) London?

7. What time of the year do you think these times were recorded?

Name _____

Mighty oaks

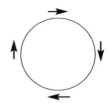

❑ A cycle is a series of events that happen in the same order over and over again. The best shape for a cycle model is a circle.

Read the text below about the oak tree and underline all the information about the tree's life cycle. Then make a large cycle model to show each stage. Decide how many sections you must divide your circle into before you start. Use words and pictures to show what happens at each stage of the cycle.

Forests of oak trees used to cover large areas of Britain and other parts of Europe. As the population grew, many of these were cut down to make way for farming and the growth of towns and cities. It remains, though, one of our most common trees, growing well on clay soil in gardens and parks as well as in traditional woodland.

There are thought to be around 800 different types of oak tree, although only two of them - the common oak and the sessile oak - are native to Britain.

The oak tree's bark tends to be grey-brown in colour and becomes rough and cracked with age. Its leaves are lobed and the acorns that contain a single seed are about two centimetres long and rest in a scaly cup.

Because of its vast size, an oak tree is able to support a great variety of wildlife in its bark, trunk and branches and in the leaf litter at its base. Birds like jays and squirrels feast on the acorns. Some of these are buried and then forgotten and, if conditions are favourable, they will start to develop into new trees. First the acorn shell splits open underground. The main root then begins to grow, searching in the soil all around for moisture and minerals. As the root system begins to expand, a shoot will start to grow through the split in the acorn and this will gradually push towards the surface of the soil. Leaves will soon grow on the shoot and from this the young sapling will develop. After many years acorns will grow on the adult oak tree and so the life cycle process will start all over again.

Oak trees produce very strong wood so their timber has always been used for building. In the past, sailing ships were made from oak and it has also been used for constructing the framework of large buildings like houses and barns.

Name _____

Floating danger

Icebergs are massive chunks of ice that float in the cold seas around the Arctic and Antarctic. They were once part of huge glaciers that form near the North and South Poles. These glaciers - made from ice hundreds of metres thick - move slowly towards the ocean. Here, when they are pounded and smashed by waves, they break and drift into the sea.

Icebergs can be as much as two kilometres long and over 70 metres high. The largest Arctic icebergs can be fantastic shapes and are known as ice islands. Scientific expeditions have camped on them for several months at a time. Icebergs from Antarctica tend to be lower and look like enormous flat tables with cliff-like edges.

Only the tip of the iceberg floats above the surface of the water. Most of it lies below the surface and therefore cannot be seen. Sizes may vary but it has been worked out that as much as eight or nine times more ice remains submerged. A further danger is the fact that because the intense cold produced by icebergs chills the air around them they can become hidden in a haze of mist.

Icebergs that float south from the Arctic region can be a great danger to shipping using the busy routes across the North Atlantic Ocean between North America and Europe.

The most famous accident involving an iceberg happened in April 1912 when a ship called the Titanic - the largest passenger liner of the time - collided with an iceberg. The ship, on its maiden voyage from Britain to New York, sank with the loss of 1,500 lives. Following the disaster, the International Ice Patrol was established to warn ships of the danger of icebergs. Special ships now constantly patrol the area breaking up small icebergs and reporting larger ones to other shipping.

1. This information about icebergs has been written in five paragraphs. Sum up the contents of each paragraph in a phrase or short sentence.

2. How can scientists tell the difference between icebergs from the North and South Poles?

3. Read paragraph three again carefully. Then draw a diagram showing the approximate shape and size of an iceberg above and below the surface of the water.

4. Give at least three reasons why icebergs are so dangerous.

5. How have these dangers largely been prevented since the accident involving the Titanic?

Name _____

The Victorians

❏ Most information books have a table of contents at the front. This can be a very useful guide when you want to find a particular aspect of the topic you are studying.

❏ Here is the contents list from a history book about the Victorians.

Contents

	Page
Who were the Victorians?	4
Queen Victoria	7
Streets and houses	11
Factories and work	16
Education	20
Religion	25
The Great Exhibition	31
Public health	39
Counting the people	45
The Crimean War	50
Trade and Empire	58
A Victorian Christmas	64

❏ Write the name of the section, and the page number on which it begins, where you would be most likely to find the answer to these questions. Some might be in more than one section.

1. Who was Queen Victoria's husband? How many children did she have?
2. Which were Britain's largest towns in Victorian times?
3. What famous event happened during the Battle of Balaklava?
4. How many people went to church in Victorian times?
5. How long did the Victorian period last?
6. Which goods did Victorian Britain export to other parts of the world?
7. Who was Florence Nightingale?
8. How many servants did wealthy people employ?
9. What did Victorian children learn at school?
10. Who first introduced Christmas trees into this country?
11. What are cholera and typhoid? How did people catch them?
12. What jobs did most Victorian children have to do?

Name _____

Sponsored run

❏ The children from Summerton School are taking part in a sponsored run to raise money for new PE equipment. For safety reasons the run is taking place in the local park.

❏ Using a coloured pencil, mark on the map the route they have to follow. The instructions are given below.

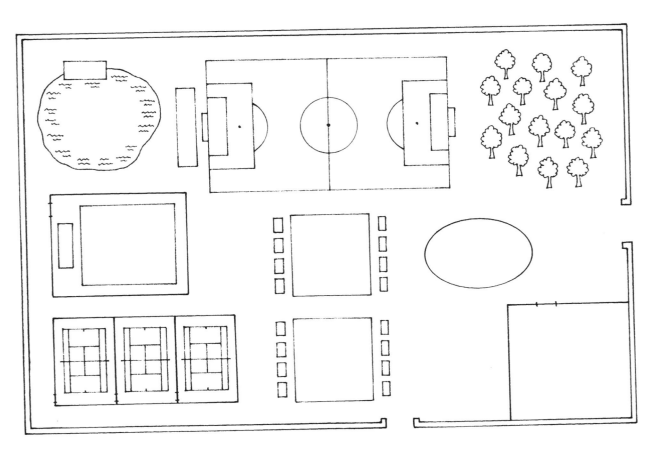

1. The run starts at the main gates to the park.
2. Turn right and run to the right of the wooded area.
3. Then run between the football pitch and the fence at the edge of the park.
4. Keep the changing rooms on your left.
5. Go round the top edge of the boating lake past the boat station.
6. Run between the bowling green and the outer fence.
7. Then turn left between the bowling green and the tennis courts.
8. Run through the gap between the two large flower beds.
9. Turn left and run between the top of the skateboard area and the football pitch.
10. Now head for the edge of the children's play area near the small gate.
11. Follow the edge of the play area fence and then the park fence until you reach the side entrance.
12. The run finishes at the side entrance.

Name _____

Riddle time

❏ Read through these descriptions carefully and identify the six things.
The objects are not named but plenty of clues are given in the description.
When you have guessed the answers see if you can add more clues of your
own to each of the objects. Draw each object.

A turn of the key sets this monster to life.
It throbs and roars but can splutter on a cold day.
Bright white eyes peer ahead into the dark.
It flashes orange when it turns.
This creature needs to drink often to keep it running.

I am a small, thin piece of paper.
My colour can vary and I will wear out quickly.
Value me and keep me in a safe place.
Hold me up to the light to view my hidden parts.
Or use me like a history book to learn more about the past.

My master waves his arms around when it blows.
Then I may tumble to the ground.
My tough skin protects me but is harmless.
I am both food and drink.
Go right to my centre to find the chance of new life.

For many years I was more important than I am today.
I produce both heat and light.
I may start long but I will end up short.
I can come in a range of different colours and smells.
Watch me well or I can be dangerous.

Like people I rise, travel and then go to bed again.
Life would not be possible without me.
Although I am far, far away you can still feel my power.
I am constantly there even though you cannot see me.
I influence how time is spent each day.

I may be sharp and spiky like a hedgehog.
But my job is to do with appearance and not with protection.
Like you, my teeth can get old and fall out.
I can be plastic or metal
I do my job by running backwards and forwards and up and down.

Name _____

Get sporty

❏ This is a plan view of the new sports store that has opened in the High Street. Using the information given at the bottom of the sheet, label each of the display areas in the new store so customers can find their way around.

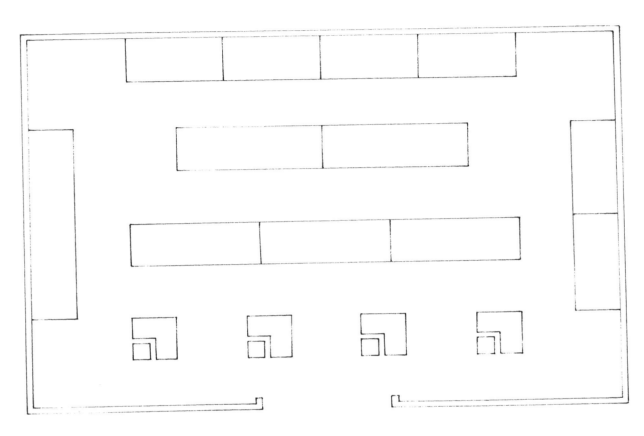

Most of the summer sports are found on the display area at the back of the store. Tennis is on the left-hand side and cricket on the right. Golf is next to cricket. Between tennis and golf is found swimming and surfing.

The bicycle display area is found on the left-hand side of the store.

There are two units next to the summer sports. Girls' and women's sports clothing is on the right-hand side and boys' and men's clothing is on the left.

On the right-hand side of the store are two units. Rugby items are closer to the main entrance and football is further away.

That leaves the block of three units that are next to the checkout area. School PE kit is displayed in the centre of this block. Roller boots are found near the bicycles and skateboards at the other end of this block.

Name _____

Busy day

❑ Below is a pie chart. These are used to show information. Why do you think they are called pie charts? This pie chart shows how Maria spends her time during one day and one night – that is a period of 24 hours. Some of the times have been rounded off to make them easier to record.

❑ Study the chart carefully and then answer the questions at the bottom of the sheet.

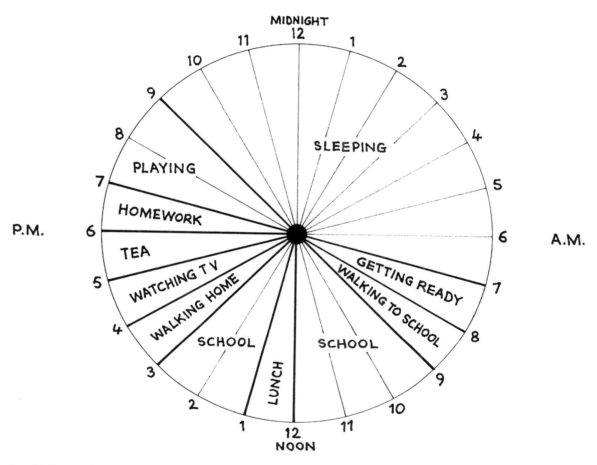

1. What does Maria spend most time doing?
2. How many hours is this?
3. What fraction of the whole day is this?
4. How long altogether does she spend eating lunch and tea? Again also give the answer as a fraction.
5. How long does Maria spend at school including lunch? Also give the answer as a fraction.
6. What time does Maria go to bed and get up?
7. How long does Maria spend playing? Also answer as a fraction.
8. How long does it take Maria to get to and from school? Also answer as a fraction.
9. Between what times does Maria do her homework?
10. How do you know this information was taken for a week day?

Name _____

Lucky find?

❑ Read the extract and then answer the questions below.

It was the shiny metal clip that first attracted Claire's attention. She had got off the bus and was just passing a row of parked vehicles when she picked up the sudden glint of metal in the corner of her eye.

On closer examination she noticed that the metal fastener was part of a large leather wallet that rested in the gutter just behind the rear wheel of a large red sports car.

She stooped down, scooped up the wallet and tucked it quickly into her sports bag before anyone on the busy pavement could notice what she was doing. She zipped up the bag and hurried off in the direction of home, keen to check on the contents of the wallet at the earliest opportunity.

When she arrived home, Claire made polite excuses downstairs and went to the security of her room as quickly as possible. Now was her chance. She removed the wallet from her bag, unclipped the fastener and looked inside.

All the wallet's compartments were crammed with banknotes. From their colours and the numbers printed on them there were tens, twenties and fifties all arranged in order and neatly folded. A quick search revealed the wallet contained no other papers of any description.

For several minutes Claire sat on the bed staring at the bundle of notes now spread out in front of her. She knew she faced a difficult dilemma and before too long important decisions would have to be made. She had heard the saying 'finders keepers' but was not sure whether she was prepared to go quite that far.

1. How did Claire make sure she was not noticed when she first picked up the wallet?

2. Later, how was Claire able to look inside the wallet privately?

3. Why was Claire unable to return the wallet to its owner straightaway? Are there any clues at all to suggest who the owner might be?

4. Explain in your own words what the phrase 'she faced a difficult dilemma' means.

5. What does the saying 'finders keepers' mean? Do you agree with this? Say yes or no and give reasons.

6. What do you think Claire will do next? What would you do if you were faced with the same situation?

Name _____

Brave Theseus

❑ This well-known legend from Ancient Greece about Theseus and the Minotaur is told in six paragraphs but they are in the wrong order. Cut out each of the paragraphs and put them in the correct order.

Princess Ariadne, the king's daughter, knew that this must stop so she persuaded a brave young soldier called Theseus to climb down into the maze to put an end to the Minotaur's bloodthirsty ways. She told him that he could escape from the maze after killing the beast if he unravelled a ball of wool as he moved through the twisting tunnels. Later he could use the thread to find his way out.

On the Greek island of Crete, the evil King Minos was protected by a large savage beast. It was called the Minotaur. Standing at over two metres high it had the body of a man and the head of a bull. Its horns and teeth were razor sharp and it liked nothing better than to feed on human flesh.

With its powerful nostrils, the Minotaur picked up Theseus' scent and charged headlong into action. But the clever warrior stepped nimbly to one side and flattened himself against the wall of the tunnel as the beast rushed by. As soon as the Minotaur had passed, Theseus drew his sword, sliced through one of the beast's legs and as it collapsed on the floor rushed in to kill it.

Each year seven boys and seven girls from the city were chosen and sent down into the maze. They tried in vain to find their way out but soon got lost and became victims of the Minotaur.

Using the wool given to him by Ariadne, Theseus found his way back out of the labyrinth, triumphantly carrying the severed head of the Minotaur. Back on the surface he threw the head at the feet of the king and proclaimed that the rule of evil was finally over.

The Minotaur lived in a series of caves and underground tunnels directly beneath the king's palace. The system of tunnels was so complicated that it was known by everyone as the labyrinth or maze.

❑ No conversation has been included in the story. Choose two of the paragraphs involving the main characters and make up your own dialogue between them. You might choose Ariadne and her father, Ariadne and Theseus or even Theseus and the Minotaur.

Name _____

The thirsty bird

❑ This is a well-known fable – a story that has a meaning.
Read the story carefully and then answer the questions.

A large crow had spent a very busy day nest building. It was now nearing the end of the day. He was tired but above all he was very thirsty and was desperate to find somewhere to get a drink of water.

No matter where he searched he was unable to find a refreshing pool of water. The more he flew round and round searching, the thirstier he became. Just when he was at his wits' end he noticed a large jug outside the back door of a small cottage.

At first he perched on a nearby tree to check that the coast was clear and when he was satisfied, he flew down and rested on the rim of the jug. He peered inside and saw that the water was right at the bottom.

First he attempted to reach the water by perching on the edge of the jar and reaching down inside, but by doing this he almost came to a sticky end. Then the crow started to tap the jug sharply with his beak in the hope of breaking it but it proved to be far too strong and well made. He also tried to push against the jug so that it would topple over forcing the water to run out, but it refused to budge.

By now, the crow was almost exhausted and even thirstier. He was just about to give up when he suddenly had a brain wave. Part of the gravel path leading up to the cottage door contained some large pebbles. Carefully he picked up a pebble in his powerful beak, flew up to the rim of the jug and dropped the pebble into the water. He repeated the process over and over again until, many trips later, the jug was nearly full of stones. Eventually he was able to perch on the edge of the jug and enjoy a long, cool refreshing drink of water. It was certainly a feather in his cap.

1. Find these phrases in the story – 'at his wits' end', 'coast was clear', 'almost came to a sticky end', 'had a brain wave', 'a feather in his cap'. Underline them with a coloured pencil. Explain what they mean.
2. List the different unsuccessful attempts the crow made to get a drink of water.
3. Explain in your own words how the crow eventually managed to drink the water.
4. What do you think is the moral or the meaning of this story?

Name _____

Favour returned

❑ Here is a fable that involves two animals. Some of the sentences have been jumbled up. Underline those sentences with a coloured pencil and then rewrite them correctly using the rest of the story to help you. When you have finished, discuss with a friend what you think the meaning or moral of the fable is.

The morning had been hectic, the afternoon was warm and the lion soon drifted off to sleep in the comfort of its den. Suddenly it felt a slight movement on its nose and, slowly opening one of its large, yellow eyes, it noticed a tiny, brown mouse sitting there. angry made lion the This very. As the lion twitched its nose the mouse fell onto the floor and the huge beast soon held the terrified creature in its powerful paw.

'What do you mean by waking me up?' roared the lion. 'going you am for kill I this to.'

The mouse was so frightened that it had difficulty speaking, but it blurted out, 'Please do not eat me. I am only a tiny mouse and would certainly not fill you up. Let me go. you do can I something Maybe to help day one.'

This amused the conceited lion. He laughed out loud as he thought how a tiny mouse could possibly be of any help to the strongest and mightiest creature in the land. However, he decided to let the mouse go and soon the relieved creature was scurrying out of the den.

close again few mouse A passed the den days to the later. This time it found the lion caught in a large net. The trap had been set by a group of local hunters. The net was made from very strong rope. struggled lion tighter the became The trap the more the.

'It is better if you lie perfectly still,' said the mouse. 'This is my chance to help you.'

began Slowly the with sharp mouse through teeth rope to chew a piece of its. For hour after hour it chewed slowly away until gradually sections of the rope began to loosen. free there enough big lion its Soon to hole get the for a was paw. With more chewing, the lion was able to move two paws and after even more hours hard work by the mouse, the lion was eventually able to struggle free from the trap.

lion For mouse rest the its always the life grateful was the of to. And the two creatures became the best of friends.

Name _____

As the saying goes

❏ Sometimes people use phrases that do not mean exactly what they say. For instance, 'to look before you leap' means to consider things carefully before you decide to do something.

❏ Explain what the phrases in bold below mean in the context of each incident.

Jason had promised Sarah that he would not tell anyone else about the plan to go to the shops to buy Mum's birthday present. But when he saw David just before they left he could not help **'letting the cat out of the bag'**.

Sunita had thought carefully about both sides of the argument but it was still a very difficult choice. Should she spend the money on the new CD she wanted or put it towards her holiday fund? She could no longer continue to **'sit on the fence'**.

Carl was fed up with his teachers and his parents always complaining about his untidy handwriting. When he went back to school after the holidays he was determined **'to turn over a new leaf'**. He bought himself a new pen and decided to practise every day.

Chloe and Rachel stopped outside the derelict house and looked in through the broken window. They had been warned about going near the building and knew they **'would be in hot water'** if their parents found out. Curiosity, however, soon got the better of them and they pulled open the damaged door and stepped inside.

Shannon had always been good at football and her bedroom was lined with all the trophies she had won during the years. Friends often asked her how good a player she was but Shannon was always very careful about what she said as Mum had told her it was not good **'to blow your own trumpet'** all the time.

Although he had tried to ignore it, the teasing in the playground continued during the next playtime. The other boys did not realise just how upset David was feeling. He wanted to let his feelings show, run over to the others and sort them out but he knew deep down that **'flying off the handle'** would not be the correct thing to do.

The two detectives made a thorough search of all the rooms inside the house as they were certain they would find a clue somewhere. The chief had urged them to look carefully inside the garage as well but they had ignored this advice as they felt it was **'barking up the wrong tree'**.

Name _____

The magic bowl

❑ Read this extract from a well-known story that comes from China and then answer the questions given below.

Shen Tan was a wealthy and powerful emperor who ruled over all of China. He was well known for his kindness and generosity and above all he liked to please his wife Mai Ling.

One day he called all his most skilled potters in front of him and said to them 'It is my wife's birthday in a few weeks time. I want you all to make the most beautiful washing bowl that you can. It must be the best in all the land and remind my wife of me whenever she washes her hands and face.'

The potters went away to their workshops and there they toiled day and night making the finest bowls they could produce. They used the best clay, shaped it well with their skilful hands, baked it in the kiln at the perfect temperature and decorated it with the brightest paints.

But when the bowls were presented to Mai Ling none of them were to her satisfaction. The potters left disappointed and Mai Ling was annoyed because she did not have a special present from the emperor on her birthday.

Several weeks later an old man arrived at the palace. The old man explained to the emperor and his wife that he had heard about the bowls and that he had come to show them one that he had made. Furthermore, he claimed it was the most precious in China. However when he opened his bag to show the couple, all he took out was a large collection of broken pieces.

Mai Ling flew into a rage. She shook her fists, stamped her feet and screamed. 'This is far worse than before. What possible use could all these broken pieces have? Guards, throw the pieces onto the rubbish tip and put this old man in jail for playing such a trick on us.'

Had she taken the trouble to examine the damaged bowl she would have noticed that the pieces that made up the base of the object spelt out a special message. It read, 'I am a magic bowl. The person who fits me together will have anything they wish...'

1. Why did the emperor want to give his wife a washing bowl?

2. List the ways in which the potters tried to make the most beautiful bowl possible.

3. What sort of person do you think Mai Ling was? Give reasons.

4. What special qualities did the broken bowl have?

5. Predict how you think the story might develop from this point. Who might find the broken pieces? Would they know what to do with them? Would Mai Ling still want a present? What might happen to the old man in jail?

Name _____

Games and sports

❑ Here is a rhyming poem about games and sports based on all the letters in the alphabet. Read through the poem and find the names of the sports and games that have been missed out. The letters will help you and there are other clues as well.

A is for _____ with arrow and bow

B is for bowling, pins all in a row.

C is for _____ on a hot summer day

D is for draughts, an indoor game you can play.

E for equestrian, all using the horse

F is for _____ my favourite of course.

G is for _____ stand the ball on a tee

H is for hockey, mind the stick on the knee.

I is for _____ all frozen and cold

J is for _____ into the sandpit, I'm told.

K is for karate, dress in a loose suit

L is for ludo, the board shows the route.

M is for motor-racing, stop on the flag

N is for _____ put the ball in the bag.

O is for orienteering with compass in hand

P is for polo, on water and land.

Q is for quoits, all round like a ring

R is for _____ 'World Champions' they sing

S is for _____ the racers get wet

T is for _____ avoid the high net

U is for umpiring, to make everything fair

V is for volleyball, keep it up in the air

W is for _____ and mind you don't run

X is for extra-time, when the game's not quite won.

Y is for _____ get the sail to extend

Z is for sleeping when the game's at an end.

Name _____

The shopping spree

❑ Maria and Sunil go to the shops with their parents. They stand outside different shops and talk about items that they can see displayed in the windows.

❑ Look carefully at their conversations and then write down the six different items they are talking about.

Maria: "That's the new one there. It's only just come out."
Sunil: "Have you heard of the author before?"
Maria: "Yes. They are so exciting I always finish them quickly."
Sunil: "Is the print clear and easy to read?"
Maria: "Yes, and there are always colourful illustrations to look at."

Sunil: "Are you sure that would be the right size for you?"
Maria: "Yes, my feet would touch the ground easily."
Sunil: "The saddle doesn't look very comfortable to me."
Maria: "No, but it does have 16 different gears to choose from."
Sunil: "Don't forget you'll need to buy a helmet as well."

Sunil: "Will that one be suitable for your system?"
Maria: "Yes, it needs to be at least a 15 inch."
Sunil: "What's wrong with the old one?"
Maria: "It's not very clear and it keeps flashing on and off."
Sunil: "This is the latest flat screen version. It should look good with your keyboard, printer and base unit."

Maria: "Which colour do you prefer?"
Sunil: "I have a blue pair already, so I am looking for something in black, although they must have a belt."
Maria: "Do you like straight legs or baggy?"
Sunil: "I think baggy are more fashionable."
Maria: "Make sure you choose the right size; some shrink when you wash them."

Sunil: "I need it when we return to school after the holidays."
Maria: "That's a good one, the box is very strong and it's got pencils in as well."
Sunil: "I have plenty of those. It's the other equipment that is important."
Maria: "Do you know how to use a compass and a protractor?"
Sunil: "Yes, and a set square, ruler and calculator."

Name _____

A simple message

❏ Haiku is a form of poetry that originated in Japan. It aims to get its message across in a simple three-line poem that does not have to rhyme. Each line is based on syllables. There should be five syllables in the first line, seven in the second and five in the third.

❏ Each of these haiku poems describes different things. What are they? Draw pictures of them.

It scurried away
to nibble the tasty cheese in
the peace of its hole.

Soft flakes falling down
as white as a jug of milk,
smooth, spotless blanket.

He's waving at me,
swishing his tail in foam spray
then toppling on sand.

Rich, dark or pure white
but always creamy and smooth,
melts now on the tongue.

Leather on leather,
it arcs through the air to nestle
safely in the net.

Hard skin, soft centre,
it hangs in the tree above
bright squidgy yellow.

Tiny pearls up high.
They twinkle from a distant
cold inky black sea.

From green to red to
brown, I change in time, before
plunging down to earth.

Name _____

Road battle

❑ Some children at Ladybrook School have been asked to write a play script about how a difficult issue might be settled. They have chosen to write about the problems caused by plans to build a new road system across open farmland near the town of Abbotswood.

❑ Here are details about some of the characters they made up and the opinions they gave in the play about the building of the new road.

David Blyth (a spokesman for Moorcroft Council): There is too much traffic in Abbotswood. Pedestrians are in danger and many of the old buildings are being literally shaken to pieces by heavy lorries.

Wendy Brown (chairperson of the governors at Abbotswood Primary School): Because of the number of vehicles that pass the school each day we have been unable to find a new crossing warden. Everyone feels the job is just too dangerous.

Ted Forrester (owner of the Tasty Snacks Café): People will drive straight past the town on the new road and not stop at my place for something to eat.

Lucy Evans (local farmer): I will lose 20 hectares of good grazing land. The cost of buying hay could put me out of business.

John Holmes (a home owner): My cottage will have to be knocked down to build the road. I have lived there happily for 15 years and I don't want to move.

Harrison Thomas (managing director of the Full Tank Petrol Company): We intend to site a new 24 hour filling station somewhere on the new road system. We want to help the motorist all we can.

Dr Tom Robinson (secretary of the Moorcroft Archaeological Society): Research shows that the land covered by the road could hold the remains of a medieval town. Precious treasures may be lost forever.

Lucy Rider (a local lorry driver): The new road is bound to help us drivers. Now it takes us ages to drive through the town. When the new road opens we will be able to deliver goods much more quickly.

❑ Make separate lists of the people or groups who are either FOR or AGAINST the new road and summarise in your own words the reasons they give in their arguments. Whose side would you be on? Explain your reasons.

Name _____

Bargain buy

❏ A new product has been launched in the shops. Here is the packet it is sold in.

1. What is the name of the new product and who makes it?

2. What special offers does the product have?

3. What slogans are used to advertise the new product?

4. Important information is given on the side of the box. What do the terms **ingredients** and **nutritional Values** mean?

5. What does the letter 'e' mean at the beginning of the weight details?

6. Give two different ways of getting in touch with the company that makes the product.

Name _____

Christmas holidays

❑ The local newsagent sends out a flyer to all its customers to tell them about the times it will be open during the Christmas holidays.

A VERY MERRY CHRISTMAS AND A PROSPEROUS NEW YEAR FROM EVERYONE AT THE ....

NEWS CABIN

We would like to thank you for your support over the past year. Please find listed below opening hours during the festive season.

December 24th (Christmas Eve)	6-00 a.m. to 5-00 p.m.
December 25th (Christmas Day)	CLOSED ALL DAY
December 26th (Boxing Day)	9-00 a.m. to 4-00 p.m.
December 27th (Saturday)	8-00 a.m. to 8-00 p.m.
December 28th (Sunday)	7-00 a.m. to 6-00 p.m.
December 29th (Monday)	7-00 a.m. to 8-00 p.m.
December 30th (Tuesday)	7-00 a.m. to 8-00 p.m.
December 31st (New Year's Eve)	7-00 a.m. to 5-00 p.m.
January 1st (New Year's Day)	10-00 a.m. to 4-00 p.m.

1. Which is the only day when the shop is completely closed?

2. Which days is the shop open for 13 hours?

3. Which day is the shop open for 11 hours?

4. Which day is the shop open for the shortest time?

5. Which is the most common opening time?

6. How long is the shop open on December 27th?

7. Why do you think the shop closes early on December 31st and opens late on January 1st?

8. Why do you think the shop opens almost everyday even though most people are home from work on holiday?

....

Name _____

Oliver's story

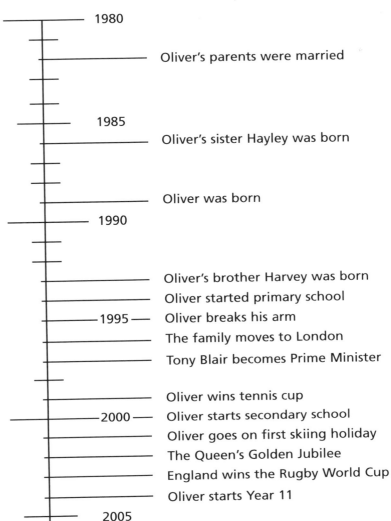

1980	
	Oliver's parents were married
1985	
	Oliver's sister Hayley was born
	Oliver was born
1990	
	Oliver's brother Harvey was born
	Oliver started primary school
1995	Oliver breaks his arm
	The family moves to London
	Tony Blair becomes Prime Minister
	Oliver wins tennis cup
2000	Oliver starts secondary school
	Oliver goes on first skiing holiday
	The Queen's Golden Jubilee
	England wins the Rugby World Cup
	Oliver starts Year 11
2005	

❑ This is a timeline showing some of the main events in the life of a boy called Oliver. Study it carefully and then answer the following questions.

1. What ages are the three children, Hayley, Oliver and Harvey at the end of 2004?
2. How much older than Oliver is Hayley?
3. How much younger than Oliver is Harvey?
4. How old was Oliver when the family moved to London?
5. How old was Oliver when he first went skiing?
6. What important event happened to Oliver in the year 2000?
7. What event did the whole country celebrate in 2002?
8. What major sporting event happened in 2003?
9. When did Tony Blair become Prime Minister?
10. What do you think is Oliver's best sport? Give reasons.
11. In what year did Oliver spend some time in hospital? Explain how you know.
12. In what year will Oliver become 18?

Name _____

Book index

❑ Most information books have an index at the end. It is arranged in alphabetical order. The index tells you the number of the page or pages on which information can be found.

❑ Here is part of an index from an information book. Use it to answer the questions given below.

Land Edwin 24
larynx 38-39 44
lasers 8 26-27 29 42 44
lenses 8 16-17 20 22-24 29
liquids 9 32
loudspeakers 40-43

magnifying glasses 22
microchips 27
microphones 36 40-42
microscopes 22-23
mirages 17
mirrors 8 14 22-23 26-27
Moon 13 27
movie cameras 25
music 40-41

1. Where would you find information on music?

2. Where would you find details on liquids?

3. What is on page 17?

4. What is on page 42?

5. How many pages are there on lenses?

6. How many pages are there on mirrors?

7. How many times is the prefix 'micro' used? What does it mean?

8. Which person's name is mentioned?

9. Where might you find out information about the human voice? How did you know?

10. Which part of the solar system is mentioned in the book?

11. Can you suggest what the title of this reference book might be?

12. What school subject might it be most useful for?

Name _____

Play the game

❏ Here are the instructions for making and playing a problem-solving game called **Hnefetafl**. Evidence has been found to suggest it may have been invented by the Vikings who used it to pass the long, dark winter evenings.

❏ Use both sections of text to make brief bullet-pointed or numbered information lists that would be suitable for printing on the box in which the game is sold. You may also want to include several simple diagrams to help explain the set up and the rules.

Setting up the game:
The board needed to play the game should be made from a large piece of thick cardboard. It should have 121 two-centimetre squares arranged in an 11 X 11 grid. Shade in the three squares in each corner to make an 'L' shape. Then obtain some playing pieces. These could be made, or coloured counters could be used. Twenty-four light coloured pieces are needed. These are called 'white'. Thirteen dark-coloured pieces will also be required. These are called 'black'. One of the black pieces needs to be larger than the rest. This is designated the 'king'.

Playing the game:
First place the white pieces anywhere in the four rows of squares at the very edge of the board but not in any of the shaded squares. Then put the king in the middle square and surround it with all the other black pieces. Black and white then take it in turns to move. Both sets of pieces can move forwards, backwards or sideways. They can move as many squares as the player wishes as long as there is nothing in their way. If they sandwich an enemy piece, i.e. one on either side of it, this has to be removed from the board. The aim of the game is for the black king to reach one of the four corner squares. While it is doing this, the white pieces try to take the black king or get in its way. White pieces are not allowed to go into the three shaded squares in each of the corners.

1. Do you think this is an easy or a difficult game to play? Give your reasons.

2. Could more than two people play the game at a time? Explain.

3. Could you make any changes to the rules to make the game easier or quicker to play? Give details.

4. What particular skills do you think are needed to play the game successfully?

Name _____

Report time

❑ Miss Butler, the class teacher of 5B, uses this chart of test results to help her write her reports at the end of the term.

❑ Each of the tests was out of 50 marks.

Child's name	English	Maths	Science
Neil	24	29	33
Mary	27	15	24
Nina	40	45	39
Rakesh	48	26	42
Ahmed	36	37	38
Maria	45	40	47
Paul	19	23	31
Sanjay	28	46	33
Stacey	17	24	26
David	36	14	39
Claire	41	29	26
Leah	40	35	37

❑ Now answer these questions:

1, 2 and 3. Which pupil scored the highest mark in each of the three subjects, English, maths and science?

4. Who was the best all-round pupil?

5. How many children scored more than half marks in maths?

6. How many boys scored more than half marks in English?

7. How many girls scored more than half marks in science?

❑ Are these statements true or false?

8. Most of the girls did better in English than in maths.

9. Most of the boys did better in science than in English.

10. Ahmed had less than half marks in each test.

11. Most of the children had over half marks in all three subjects.

12. Maria only dropped a total of twenty marks in the three tests.

Name _____

Sunny weather

❑ These line graphs show the average monthly temperatures in the cities of London, the capital of England, and Cairo, the capital of Egypt. Points have been joined together to show how the temperatures rise and fall. Study the graphs carefully and then answer the questions below.

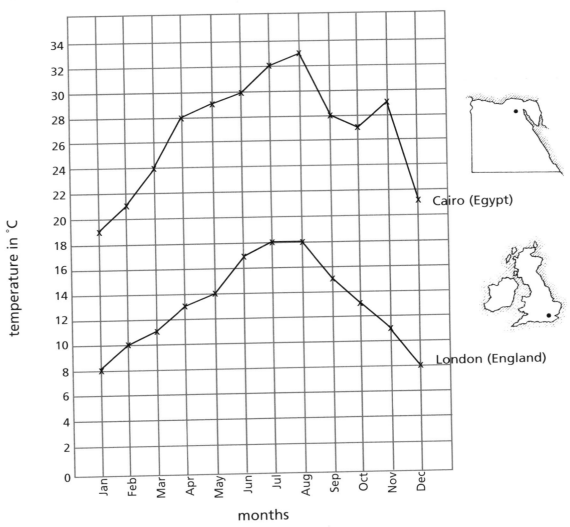

1. What scale is being used on the graphs?

2. Which months gives the highest temperature in each country?

3. Which months gives the lowest temperature in each country?

4. Which months are the most similar in both countries?

5. Which months show the greatest difference?

6. Compare the shapes of the two graphs. In what ways are the rise and fall of temperature shown on the graphs similar and/or different?

7. Why do you think Egypt is a popular country for tourists to visit? Give reasons.

8. If you were planning a visit to Egypt, in which month would you go? Explain your answer.

Name _____

Famous composers

❑ The boxes below show the years in which eight famous musical composers were born and died.
❑ Use the information to answer the questions given at the bottom of the sheet.

BEETHOVEN 1770 – 1827

ELGAR 1857 – 1934

HANDEL 1685 – 1759

BACH 1685 – 1750

GRIEG 1843 – 1907

MOZART 1756 – 1791

STRAVINSKY 1882 – 1971

DVORÂK 1841 – 1904

1. Which composer was born earliest?

2. Which composer died most recently?

3. Which composer lived to the greatest age?

4. How old was Bach when he died?

5. Which composer died at the age of 89?

6. Which composer died at the age of 35?

7. Which composers were living when Beethoven died in 1827?

8. Which composers were alive in 1700?

9. Which composers lived during the twentieth century?

10. Was Handel alive when Mozart was born?

11. Was Stravinsky alive when Elgar died?

12. Use their birth dates to place the composers in chronological order, starting farthest away in time.

Name _____

Fly the flag

Uzbekistan is an Asian country with a population of over twenty million people. It covers an area of about four hundred and fifty thousand square kilometres and one of the country's main landmarks is the inland Aral Sea. The capital city is called Tashkent.

Below is a description of the country's national flag. Read it carefully and then draw the flag showing the correct layout, symbols and colours in the large rectangular box at the bottom of the sheet.

The national flag of Uzbekistan is divided into three equal horizontal bands. The top band is blue, the central band is white and the bottom band is green. The central white band has a thin red border at the top and bottom but not on the sides.

Certain symbols are shown in the blue band on the left-hand side of the flag. Closest to the outer edge is a white crescent moon. To the right-hand side of this are a total of 12 small white stars. There are five on the bottom row, nearest the red border, four in the centre row and three at the top. The sloping side of the trapezium that these stars form is nearest to the crescent moon.

Name _____

Food chains

❏ A food chain is the **transfer** of **energy** from plants to animals that eat them, and their **predators**.

❏ Here are three examples of food chains.

grass ——————→ rabbit ——————→ fox

grass ——————→ zebra ——————→ lion

leaf ——————→ aphid ——————→ sparrow ——————→ sparrowhawk

❏ Food chains can be used as a way of grouping living organisms.

Producers	make their own food	e.g. green plants
Consumers		
herbivores	eat plants	e.g. cows and sheep
omnivores	eat plants and meat	e.g. some humans
carnivores	eat meat	e.g. foxes and lions
Decomposers	break down dead or decaying matter	e.g. fungi, bacteria, slugs, millipedes

Now answer these questions:

1. Explain the meaning of the words in bold print.

2. In the food chains, what words might be used in place of the arrows?

3. Do the food chains have anything in common with each other? Explain

4. What comes at the bottom of all food chains?

5. Give other examples of **producers, consumers** and **decomposers**.

6. In the section on omnivores why is the phrase 'some humans' used?